PRIMARY MATHEMATICS 5B
WORKBOOK

Primary Mathematics Project Team

Project Director
Dr Kho Tek Hong

Team Members
Chee Kum Hoong, Hector
Liang Hin Hoon
Lim Eng Tann
Lim Hui Cheng, Rosalind
Ng Hwee Wan
Ng Siew Lee

Curriculum Specialists
Cheong Ngan Peng, Christina
Ho Juan Beng

**Curriculum Planning & Development Division
Ministry of Education, Singapore**

**FEDERAL
PUBLICATIONS**

Original edition published under the title Primary Mathematics Workbook 5B
© 1984 Curriculum Planning & Development Division
Ministry of Education, Singapore
Published by Times Media Private Limited
This American Edition
© 2003 Times Media Private Limited

Times Media Private Limited
A member of Times Publishing Limited
Times Centre, 1 New Industrial Road
Singapore 536196
Customer Service Hotline: (65) 6213 9106
E-mail: fps@tpl.com.sg
Website: www.timesone.com.sg/fpl

Distributed by
SingaporeMath.com Inc
404 Beavercreek Road #225
Oregon City, OR 97045
U.S.A.
Website: http://www.singaporemath.com

First published 2003
Reprinted 2003
Second impression 2004

ISBN 981-01-8513-8

Printed in Singapore by C.O.S. Printers Pte Ltd

ACKNOWLEDGEMENTS

The project team would like to record their thanks to the following:

- members of the Primary Mathematics Team who developed the first edition and second edition of the package
- members of the Steering Committee for the second edition of the package
- teachers who tested the materials in the package and provided useful insights and suggestions
- Educational Technology Division, for the design and production of the audio-visual components of the package
- all those who have helped in one way or another in the development and production of the package

Our special thanks to Richard Askey, Professor of Mathematics (University of Wisconsin, Madison), Yoram Sagher, Professor of Mathematics (University of Illinois, Chicago), and Madge Goldman, President (Gabriella and Paul Rosenbaum Foundation), for their indispensable advice and suggestions in the production of Primary Mathematics (U.S. Edition).

CONTENTS

EXERCISE 1

1. Fill in the blanks.

(a)

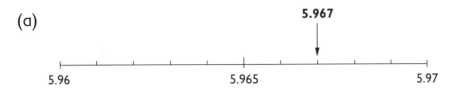

5.967 is _____ when rounded off to 2 decimal places.

(b)

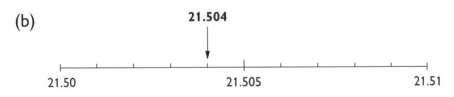

21.504 is _____ when rounded off to 2 decimal places.

(c)

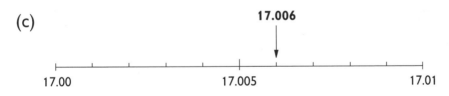

17.006 is _____ when rounded off to 2 decimal places.

2. Round off each of the following to 2 decimal places.

0.079   2.307   4.084   3.255   1.802
0.008   3.023   4.035   3.661   1.206

Shade the spaces which contain the answers. If your answers are correct, you will see a fish.

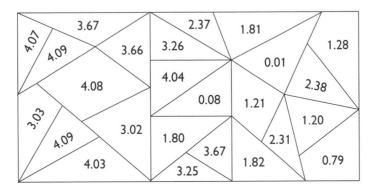

5

EXERCISE 2

1. Find the value of each of the following correct to 2 decimal places.

(a) $70 \div 9 \approx$ $9\overline{)70}$	(b) $18.01 \div 4 \approx$
(c) $21.68 \div 5 \approx$	(d) $41.53 \div 6 \approx$
(e) $0.53 \div 7 \approx$	(f) $24.05 \div 8 \approx$

2. Maria has 30 m of raffia. She used 3.15 m to tie a package. She cut the remaining part of the raffia equally into 6 pieces to make flower pot holders. How much raffia did she use for each flower pot holder? Give your answer in meters correct to 2 decimal places.

3. Adam mixed 3.46 lb of dried mangoes with twice as much dried apples. He packed the mixture into 9 bags. How much dried fruit was there in each bag? Give your answer in pounds correct to 2 decimal places.

EXERCISE 3

1. Express each fraction as a decimal correct to 2 decimal places.

(a) $\frac{8}{9} \approx$

$$9\overline{)8}$$

(b) $\frac{3}{7} \approx$

(c) $\frac{2}{3} \approx$

(d) $4\frac{1}{6} \approx$

(e) $5\frac{5}{8} \approx$

(f) $9\frac{1}{7} \approx$

EXERCISE 4

1. Multiply.

(a) $0.03 \times 10 =$	(b) $0.009 \times 10 =$
(c) $0.067 \times 10 =$	(d) $0.84 \times 10 =$
(e) $2.9 \times 10 =$	(f) $0.321 \times 10 =$
(g) $5.24 \times 10 =$	(h) $35.4 \times 10 =$
(i) $6.015 \times 10 =$	(j) $412.8 \times 10 =$

2. Multiply.

(a) $0.09 \times 20 = 0.18 \times 10$

$$= $$

(b) $3.2 \times 40 =$

(c) $4.63 \times 60 =$

(d) $22.9 \times 80 =$

(e) $12.4 \times 90 =$

9

EXERCISE 5

1. Complete the following table.

Number	× 10	× 100	× 1000
0.324			
1.635			
3.004			
8.19			
20.4			

2. Multiply.

(a) $6.166 \times 100 =$	(b) $2.009 \times 100 =$
(c) $100 \times 5.201 =$	(d) $100 \times 3.065 =$
(e) $0.072 \times 1000 =$	(f) $8.625 \times 1000 =$
(g) $1000 \times 4.86 =$	(h) $1000 \times 3.7 =$

3. Find the missing numbers.

(a) $2.68 \times \underline{\hspace{1.5cm}} = 26.8$	(b) $\underline{\hspace{1.5cm}} \times 0.8 = 8$
(c) $1.042 \times \underline{\hspace{1.5cm}} = 104.2$	(d) $\underline{\hspace{1.5cm}} \times 1.43 = 1430$
(e) $32.64 \times \underline{\hspace{1.5cm}} = 326.4$	(f) $\underline{\hspace{1.5cm}} \times 0.9 = 900$
(g) $4.125 \times \underline{\hspace{1.5cm}} = 4125$	(h) $\underline{\hspace{1.5cm}} \times 3.95 = 395$
(i) $6.9 \times \underline{\hspace{1.5cm}} = 690$	(j) $\underline{\hspace{1.5cm}} \times 0.731 = 731$

EXERCISE 6

1. Multiply.

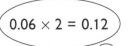

(a) 0.06 × 200 = 0.12 × 100 =
(b) 0.34 × 300 =
(c) 6.8 × 400 =
(d) 3.12 × 500 =
(e) 64.5 × 6000 =
(f) 32.08 × 7000 =
(g) 9.54 × 8000 =
(h) 3.24 × 9000 =

EXERCISE 7

1. Divide.

(a) 6 ÷ 10 =	(b) 0.3 ÷ 10 =
(c) 0.05 ÷ 10 =	(d) 0.34 ÷ 10 =
(e) 1.2 ÷ 10 =	(f) 19 ÷ 10 =
(g) 20.5 ÷ 10 =	(h) 3.65 ÷ 10 =
(i) 239 ÷ 10 =	(j) 0.58 ÷ 10 =

2. Divide.

(a) 0.8 ÷ 20 = 0.4 ÷ 10

   =

(b) 3.7 ÷ 50 =

(c) 5.34 ÷ 60 =

(d) 82.08 ÷ 90 =

(e) 29.61 ÷ 70 =

EXERCISE 8

1. Complete the following table.

Number	÷ 10	÷ 100	÷ 1000
203			
8			
7050			
58			
1458			

2. Divide.

(a) $54 \div 100 =$	(b) $20.3 \div 100 =$
(c) $2820 \div 100 =$	(d) $3.4 \div 100 =$
(e) $4525 \div 1000 =$	(f) $3400 \div 1000 =$
(g) $73 \div 1000 =$	(h) $2 \div 1000 =$

3. Find the missing numbers.

(a) $6.7 \div$ _____ $= 0.67$	(b) $80 \div$ _____ $= 0.8$
(c) $5040 \div$ _____ $= 5.04$	(d) $56.8 \div$ _____ $= 0.568$
(e) $29 \div$ _____ $= 0.029$	(f) $3.18 \div$ _____ $= 0.318$
(g) $153 \div$ _____ $= 1.53$	(h) $900 \div$ _____ $= 0.9$
(i) $46 \div$ _____ $= 4.6$	(j) $608 \div$ _____ $= 0.608$

EXERCISE 9

1. Divide.

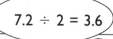

(a) 7.2 ÷ 200 = 3.6 ÷ 100

             =

(b) 9 ÷ 300 =

(c) 95.4 ÷ 900 =

(d) 57.6 ÷ 800 =

(e) 18 ÷ 6000 =

(f) 65 ÷ 5000 =

(g) 392 ÷ 4000 =

(h) 847 ÷ 7000 =

EXERCISE 10

1. Estimate the value of each of the following:

(a) $39.57 \times 48 \approx 40 \times 50$

$$=$$

(b) $21.68 \times 61 \approx$

(c) $42.07 \times 32 \approx$

(d) $68.35 \times 29 \approx$

(e) $52.46 \times 38 \approx$

EXERCISE 11

1. Multiply.

(a) $4.8 \times 23 =$ 4.8 $\underline{\times 23}$	(b) $6.51 \times 37 =$
(c) $23.97 \times 52 =$	(d) $705.8 \times 45 =$
(e) $0.59 \times 86 =$	(f) $3.09 \times 34 =$
(g) $16.47 \times 91 =$	(h) $72.15 \times 67 =$

2. Multiply.

1.8 × 12	0.74 × 34	2.53 × 29
46.6 × 67	0.92 × 53	0.58 × 91
1.86 × 25	7.39 × 48	42.08 × 36

Shade the spaces which contain the answers to the above. You will find the prize Andrew won.

Andrew

251.6	46.55	4.98	265.14	216	489.72
21.6	73.92	3122.2	48.76	45.83	527.8
500	25.16	73.37	354.72	52.78	1540.8
	128.54	312.32	553.09	46.5	354.72
		37.8			1514.88

T-shirt

watch

Andrew's prize is a _____.

17

EXERCISE 12

1.   Find the equivalent measures.

(a) 0.4 km = _____ m	(b) 1.5 km = _____ m
(c) 0.09 kg = _____ g	(d) 0.43 m = _____ cm
(e) 1.25 ft = _____ ft _____ in.	(f) 4.75 lb = _____ lb _____ oz
(g) 3.04 km = _____ km _____ m	(h) 3.8 ℓ = _____ ℓ _____ ml

EXERCISE 13

1.   Find the equivalent measures. Express each answer as a decimal.

(a) 6 g = _____ kg	(b) 8 cm = _____ m
(c) 40 ml = _____ ℓ	(d) 54 m = _____ km
(e) 2 kg 300 g = _____ kg	(f) 3 m 50 cm = _____ m
(g) 4 km 30 m = _____ km	(h) 2 ℓ 600 ml = _____ ℓ

EXERCISE 14

1. Find the equivalent measures. Express each answer as a decimal.

(a) 250 cm = _____ m

(b) 1080 g = _____ kg

(c) 3006 m = _____ km

(d) 2400 g = _____ kg

(e) 14 c = _____ qt

(f) 345 cm = _____ m

(g) 231 in. = _____ ft

(h) 3245 ml = _____ ℓ

REVIEW 1

Write the answers in the boxes.

1. Write the following in words.
   (a) 700,248

   _____

   (b) 2,109,035

   _____

2. Write the following in figures.
   (a) Eight hundred sixty thousand, seven hundred nine

   _____

   (b) Three million, forty

   _____

3. (a) What number is 0.01 more than 6.99?

   _____

   (b) What number is 0.01 more than 4.2?

   _____

4. (a) What number must be added to 634 to give the answer 1000?

   _____

   (b) What number must be added to 0.463 to give the answer 1?

   _____

5. (a) List all the factors of 100.

   _____

   (b) Which one of the following numbers is a common factor of 45 and 144?

      4,   5,   9,   45

   _____

(c) Write down the first two common multiples of 5 and 8.

6. What is the missing number in each ■?

(a) $160,000 + ■ + 80 = 167,080$

(b) $776,085 - ■ = 746,085$

(c) $1000 \times ■ = 400,000$

(d) $309,400 \div ■ = 3094$

7. Express each fraction as a decimal.

(a) $2\frac{7}{10} = $

(b) $\frac{308}{100} = $

(c) $1\frac{3}{5} = $

(d) $\frac{7}{4} = $

8. Which one of the following is greater than 2 but less than 3?

$\frac{10}{3}, \quad \frac{9}{5}, \quad \frac{11}{4}, \quad \frac{6}{2}$

9. Arrange the fractions in order, beginning with the greatest.

$\frac{5}{3}, \quad \frac{7}{12}, \quad 2\frac{1}{2}, \quad \frac{5}{8}$

10. Write −, +, × or ÷ in each ◯.

(a) $82.72 \bigcirc 10 = 72.72$

(b) $4.6 \bigcirc 100 = 104.6$

(c) $3.64 \bigcirc 10 = 36.4$

(d) $28.6 \bigcirc 100 = 0.286$

11. Find the product of 5000 and 800.

12. Find the product of $\frac{4}{5}$ and $\frac{5}{8}$.

13. Write the missing numbers.

   (a) 0.25 m = [   ] cm   (b) 2.4 kg = [   ] g

14. Write the missing decimals.

   (a) 580 g = [   ] kg   (b) 4600 m = [   ] km

   (c) 2 ℓ 4 ml = [   ] ℓ

15. Out of 1024 people in a theater, 425 are men, 480 are women and the rest are children. How many more adults than children are there?

   [   ]

16.

   Jean bought 2 shirts and 3 T-shirts. How much did she pay altogether?

   [   ]

17. There are 35 children in a class. $\frac{3}{5}$ of them can swim. How many children cannot swim?

   [   ]

18. A piece of ribbon $\frac{2}{5}$ m long is cut into 4 equal pieces. Find the length of each piece in meters.

   [   ]

19. Amy bought 10 m of cloth. She used 2.35 m of the cloth to make an apron. She cut the remaining cloth into 5 equal pieces. Find the length of each piece in meters.

   [   ]

20.

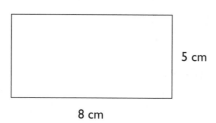

5 cm

8 cm

Find the ratio of the length to the perimeter of the rectangle. Give the answer in its simplest form.

21. Find the area of the shaded triangle.

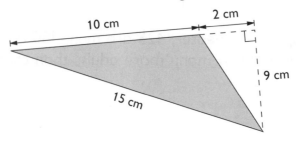

2 cm

10 cm

9 cm

15 cm

22. The figure is made up of a rectangle and a triangle. Find the area of the figure.

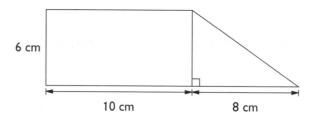

6 cm

10 cm

8 cm

23. String A is 30 cm longer than String B. String B is 60 cm longer than String C. The total length of the three strings is 3 m. Find the length of String C.

24. Adam bought 8 note pads at $1.45 each and 10 towels. He gave the cashier $100 and received $46 change. Find the cost of a towel.

---

25. A group of children went swimming. $\frac{3}{8}$ of them were girls. If there were 40 boys, how many children were there altogether?

---

26. Three boys, Juan, Seth and Jared shared a number of stamps in the ratio 3 : 5 : 7. If Seth received 45 stamps, how many more stamps did Jared receive than Juan?

EXERCISE 15

1. In each of the following, the whole is divided into 100 equal parts. What percentage of the whole is shaded?

(a)

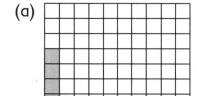

_____ %

(b)

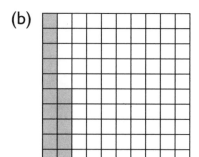

_____ %

(c)

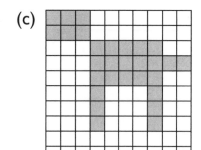

_____ %

(d)

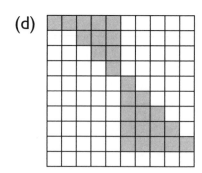

_____ %

(e)

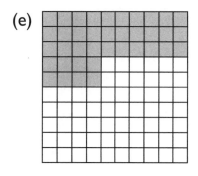

_____ %

(f)

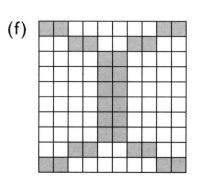

_____ %

2. In each of the following, the whole is divided into 100 equal parts.

(a) Shade 80% of the whole.

(b) Shade 63% of the whole.

3. Express each fraction as a percentage.

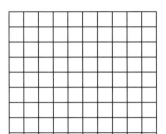

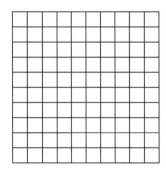

$\dfrac{87}{100} =$	$\dfrac{5}{100} =$
$\dfrac{16}{100} =$	$\dfrac{71}{100} =$
$\dfrac{68}{100} =$	$\dfrac{50}{100} =$
$\dfrac{99}{100} =$	$\dfrac{100}{100} =$

4. Fill in the missing numerator or denominator.

$7\% = \dfrac{}{100}$	$1\% = \dfrac{}{100}$
$43\% = \dfrac{}{100}$	$99\% = \dfrac{}{100}$
$14\% = \dfrac{14}{}$	$68\% = \dfrac{68}{}$
$5\% = \dfrac{5}{}$	$84\% = \dfrac{84}{}$

EXERCISE 16

1.   Express each decimal as a percentage.

(a) 0.15 =	(b) 0.86 =
(c) 0.4 =	(d) 0.9 =
(e) 0.47 =	(f) 0.12 =
(g) 0.04 =	(h) 0.5 =
(i) 0.75 =	(j) 0.06 =

2. Express each percentage as a decimal.

(a) 24% =	(b) 37% =
(c) 78% =	(d) 6% =
(e) 62% =	(f) 53% =
(g) 10% =	(h) 7% =
(i) 80% =	(j) 90% =

EXERCISE 17

1. Express each percentage as a fraction in its simplest form.

(a) $22\% = \dfrac{22}{100}$ $=$	(b) $45\% =$
(c) $96\% =$	(d) $52\% =$
(e) $6\% =$	(f) $40\% =$
(g) $90\% =$	(h) $8\% =$
(i) $75\% =$	(j) $50\% =$

EXERCISE 18

1.   Express each fraction as a percentage.

(a) $\frac{1}{2}$ =	(b) $\frac{9}{50}$ =
(c) $\frac{17}{20}$ =	(d) $\frac{12}{25}$ =
(e) $\frac{3}{5}$ =	(f) $\frac{9}{15}$ =
(g) $\frac{8}{50}$ =	(h) $\frac{3}{12}$ =
(i) $\frac{18}{75}$ =	(j) $\frac{12}{40}$ =

2. Write each of the following as a percentage.

(a) 8 out of 40

$$\frac{8}{40} = \frac{2}{10}$$

$$=$$

(b) 40 out of 80

(c) 15 out of 50

(d) 7 out of 20

(e) 24 out of 40

EXERCISE 19

1. Write each of the following as a percentage.

(a) 186 out of 200

$$\frac{186}{200} = \frac{93}{100}$$

$$=$$

(b) 39 out of 300

(c) 96 out of 400

(d) 235 out of 500

(e) 122 out of 200

---

2.   Sara mailed 20 Christmas cards. 9 of them were mailed to Canada. What percentage of the cards were mailed to Canada?

3.   There are 80 members in a school band. 24 of them are 6th grade students. What percentage of the members are 6th grade students?

4.   There are 200 units in an apartment complex. 64 of them are three-bedroom apartments. What percentage of the apartments are three-bedroom apartments?

EXERCISE 20

1.   Jane made 50 cookies. 24 of them were chocolate cookies. The rest were sugar cookies.
      (a)   What percentage of the cookies were chocolate cookies?
      (b)   What percentage of the cookies were sugar cookies?

---

2.   Ryan had $80. He spent $32 on a book.
      (a)   What percentage of his money did he spend on the book?
      (b)   What percentage of his money had he left?

3.   There are 400 seats in a concert hall. 120 of them are occupied.
      (a)   What percentage of the seats are occupied?
      (b)   What percentage of the seats are not occupied?

---

4.   125 swimmers take part in a swimming competition. 85 of them are females.
      (a)   What percentage of the swimmers are females?
      (b)   What percentage of the swimmers are males?

EXERCISE 21

1.   Find the value of each of the following:

(a)   4% of 300
 	
    =
	(b) 72% of 150
	
	    =

(c)   30% of $94
 	
    =
	(d) 5% of $250
	
	    =

(e)   25% of 240 m
 	
    =
	(f) 80% of 25 kg
	
	    =

2. Molly paid $85 last month for her utilities. 55% of this amount was for electricity. How much did Molly pay for electricity?

3. There were 48 traffic accidents in May last year. 25% of them happened on the freeways. How many accidents happened on the freeways?

4. Stephanie earns $750 a month. She gives 30% of the money to charity. How much money does Stephanie give to charity?

EXERCISE 22

1. There are 55 apples in a box. 40% of them are red apples and the rest are green apples. How many green apples are there in the box?

2. Mingfa had $840. He gave 30% of the money to his parents. How much money had he left for himself?

3.   Mike earns $1200 a month. He saves 15% of the money and spends the rest. How much does he spend each month?

---

4.   There were 750 questions in a mathematics book. Sam answered 82% of them correctly. How many questions did he answer incorrectly?

EXERCISE 23

1.　Kate has $1800 in a savings bank. The bank pays 6% interest per year.
　(a) How much interest will she earn after 1 year?
　(b) How much money will she have in the bank after 1 year?

2.　Alicia borrows $2800 from a bank. The bank charges 8% interest per year. If she pays off the loan in 1 year, how much does she have to pay?

3. The usual price of a clock was $60. At a sale, it was sold at a discount of 20%.
   (a) How much was the discount?
   (b) Find the selling price of the clock.

---

4. The usual price of a photo album was $15. It was sold at a discount of 25%. Find the selling price of the photo album.

EXERCISE 24

1. A man rents a room for $300 a month. If the rent is increased by 12%, how much more does he have to pay each month?

2. A factory had 1500 workers last year. This year, the number of workers was increased by 4%. Find the number of workers after the increase.

EXERCISE 25

1.   Find the average of each of the following:

(a) 3, 8 and 7

$$3 + 8 + 7 = 18$$

The sum is _____ .

$$18 \div 3 =$$

The average is _____ .

(b) 45 and 33

(c) 24, 38 and 19

(d) 20, 18, 36 and 98

2. This picture graph shows the number of kites made by 4 boys.

Ben	🪁 🪁 🪁 🪁 🪁 🪁
Ramat	🪁 🪁 🪁 🪁 🪁 🪁 🪁 🪁 🪁
Rosli	🪁 🪁 🪁 🪁 🪁
David	🪁 🪁 🪁 🪁 🪁 🪁 🪁 🪁

Find the average number of kites each boy made.

3. This table shows the amount of money saved by 4 girls.

Devi	Meiling	Maria	Lily
$25	$18	$32	$29

Find their average savings.

EXERCISE 26

1. Find the average of each of the following:

(a) $3.70, $4.25 and $4.50

(b) 12.5 m, 14.7 m and 12.4 m

(c) 15.5 kg, 12 kg, 14.3 kg and 16.6 kg

(d) 430 ℓ and 22 ℓ

2. This table shows the shot put results of 4 boys. Find the average result.

Ian	3.8 yd
Adam	5 yd
Pablo	5.42 yd
Jim	4.5 yd

3.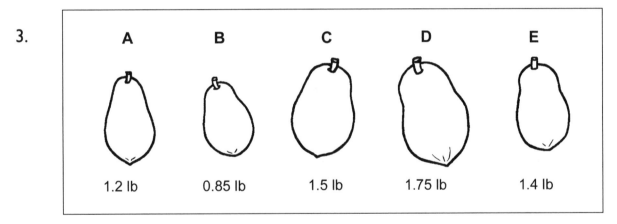

A	B	C	D	E
1.2 lb	0.85 lb	1.5 lb	1.75 lb	1.4 lb

Find the average weight of the papayas.

EXERCISE 27

1.   From Monday to Wednesday, Alex sold 258 plums altogether. What was the average number of plums he sold per day?

2.   The total weight of 8 onions is 720 g. What is their average weight?

3.   The average of 3 numbers is 12.4. Find the sum of the numbers.

4.   The average length of 4 pieces of ribbon is 28.5 in. Find their total length.

EXERCISE 28

Fill in the blanks.

1. (a) 3 m 20 cm × 4 = _____ m _____ cm

          /   \
     3 m   20 cm

Multiply the meters.
Then multiply the centimeters.

    (b) 85 cm × 3 = _____ cm

               = _____ m _____ cm

    (c) 2 m 85 cm × 3 = _____ m _____ cm

          /   \
     2 m   85 cm   = _____ m _____ cm

2. (a) 2 ℓ 150 ml × 5 = _____ ℓ _____ ml

         /   \
     2 ℓ   150 ml

    (b) 400 ml × 4   = _____ ml

               = _____ ℓ _____ ml

    (c) 3 ℓ 400 ml × 4 = _____ ℓ _____ ml

         /   \
     3 ℓ   400 ml   = _____ ℓ _____ ml

Fill in the blanks.

3.　(a)　4 km 250 m ÷ 2 = _____ km _____ m

　　　　　　　／　＼
　　　　　4 km　250 m

Divide the kilometers.
Then divide the meters.

　　(b)　1 km 200 m ÷ 3 = 1200 m ÷ 3

　　　　　　　　　　= _____ m

　　(c)　4 km 200 m ÷ 3 = _____ km _____ m

　　　　　　　／　＼
　　　　　3 km　1 km 200 m
　　　　　　　　　(1200 m)

4.　(a)　6 h 45 min ÷ 3 = _____ h _____ min

　　　　　　　／　＼
　　　　　6 h　45 min

　　(b)　1 h 20 min ÷ 4 = 80 min ÷ 4

　　　　　　　　　　= _____ min

　　(c)　5 h 20 min ÷ 4 = _____ h _____ min

　　　　　　　／　＼
　　　　　4 h　1 h 20 min
　　　　　　　　(80 min)

EXERCISE 29

1. The total weight of 4 bags of flour is 9 kg 400 g. Find their average weight.

_____

2. There are 6 containers. The average amount of water in each container is 2 ℓ 250 ml. Find the total amount of water in the 6 containers.

EXERCISE 30

1.   The average weight of Ali, Mingfa and Samy is 45 kg. Ali and Mingfa together weigh 85 kg. Find Samy's weight.

---

2.   Peter spent an average of $4.50 per day from Monday to Saturday. He spent $5.20 on Sunday.
     What was the average amount of money he spent per day from Monday to Sunday?

EXERCISE 31

1. Find the rate for each of the following:

(a) Jerome pays $225 to rent a hotel room for 3 days. The rate is $ _____ per day.	Rate = $\dfrac{225}{3}$ =
(b) Steve types 750 words in 15 minutes. The rate is _____ words per minute.	Rate =
(c) A machine fills 240 jars with jam in 20 minutes. The rate is _____ jars per minute.	Rate =
(d) A motorcycle can travel a distance of 102 mi on 3 gal of gas. The rate is _____ mi per gallon.	Rate =

EXERCISE 32

1. Fill in the blanks.

    (a) A machine makes 45 cakes per minute.

    At this rate, it will make _____ cakes in 5 minutes.

    (b) Carpets are sold at $225 per m^2.

    At this rate, a carpet of area 35 m^2 will cost $ _____.

    (c) Ben lays 25 bricks per hour.

    At this rate, he will lay _____ bricks in 7 hours.

    (d) Matthew's family uses 24 m^3 of water per month.

    At this rate, the family will use _____ m^3 of water in 6 months.

EXERCISE 33

1.   There are 2000 words on a page. How long will Alice take to read the page if she reads at the rate of 100 words per minute?

2.   The room rate at Sunshine Hotel is $80 per day. At this rate, how many days did Ben stay at the hotel if he paid $400?

3.   A wheel makes 6 revolutions per minute. At this rate, how long will it take to make 45 revolutions?

4. The workers in a factory were paid at the rate of $6 per hour. Justin worked for 7 hours. How much was he paid?

---

5. A machine can make 200 loaves of bread per minute. At this rate, how many loaves of bread can the machine make in 5 minutes?

---

6. A car can travel 12 km on 1 liter of gas. At this rate, how much gas will be used if the car travels a distance of 180 km?

EXERCISE 34

1. A taxi driver earns $300 in 5 days.

   The rate is $ _____ per day.

   (a) At this rate, he will earn $ _____ in 6 days.

   (b) He will take _____ days to earn $1200.

2. A car travels 84 km on 6 liters of gas.

   The rate is _____ km per liter.

   (a) At this rate, it can travel _____ km on 16 liters of gas.

   (b) It can travel 210 km on _____ liters of gas.

3. The cost of cementing a courtyard of area 40 m^2 is $1600.

   The rate is $ _____ per m^2.

   (a) At this rate, the cost of cementing an area of 90 m^2 is $ _____.

   (b) The cost of cementing an area of _____ m^2 is $2000.

4. A printing machine can roll out 600 pages of printed material in 4 minutes.

   The rate is _____ pages per minute.

   (a) At this rate, the machine can roll out _____ pages in 15 minutes.

   (b) It will take the machine _____ minutes to roll out 750 pages.

5.   A watch loses time at a rate of 80 seconds in 2 days.
    (a)   How many seconds will it lose in 3 days?
    (b)   How long will it take to lose 200 seconds?

---

6.   A machine can bind 1500 books in 12 minutes.
    (a)   How many books can it bind in 5 minutes?
    (b)   How long will it take to bind 1000 books?

EXERCISE 35

1. This table shows the rates of charges for renting bicycles.

First hour	$3
Every additional hour	$2

(a) Jacob rented a bicycle for 2 hours. How much should he pay?

(b) Jackie rented a bicycle from 2:00 p.m. to 6:00 p.m. How much should she pay?

(c) Four boys rented 2 bicycles for 3 hours. If they shared the cost equally, how much should each boy pay?

2. This table shows the rates of charges for water consumption in a month.

First 20 m³	$0.56 per m³
Next 20 m³	$0.80 per m³
Additional amount above 40 m³	$1.17 per m³

(a) What is the charge for 15 m³ of water used in a month?

(b) What is the charge for 30 m³ of water used in a month?

(c) What is the charge for 45 m³ of water used in a month?

EXERCISE 36

1.   The line graph shows the enrollment of a school for 4 years. Study the graph and answer the questions which follow.

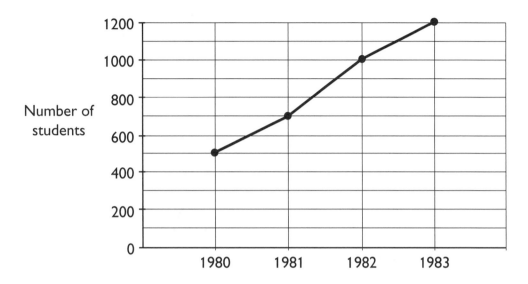

(a) What was the increase in enrollment from 1982 to 1983?

(b) When did the enrollment increase by 300 students in one year?

(c) What was the difference between the enrollment in 1980 and the enrollment in 1983?

(d) What was the total enrollment in the 4 years?

(e) What was the average enrollment per year?

2. The line graph shows the daily sales of ice-cream cones by a shop over 1 week. Study the graph and answer the questions which follow.

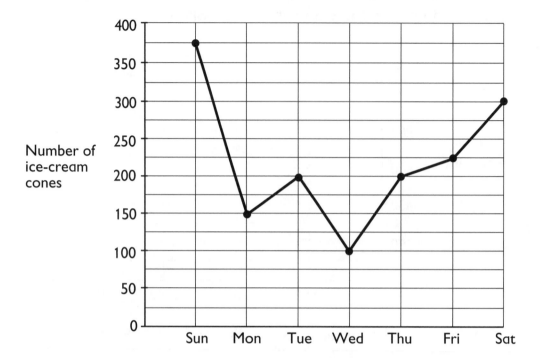

(a) On which day was the sales the lowest?

(b) What was the sales on Sunday?

(c) On which day were 300 ice-cream cones sold?

(d) What was the increase in the sales from Friday to Saturday?

(e) When did the sales decrease by 100 in 1 day?

3. The line graph shows the height of a plant measured at 8 a.m. every day for 5 days. Study the graph and answer the questions which follow.

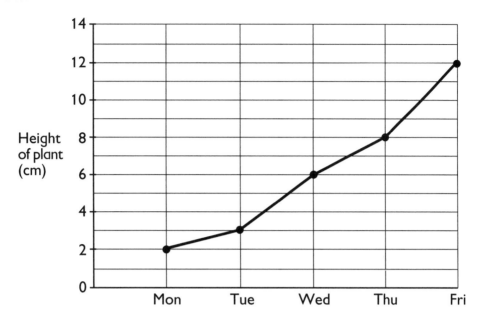

(a) What was the height of the plant measured on Tuesday?

(b) What was the increase in the height of the plant from Thursday to Friday?

(c) When did the plant grow by 3 cm in 1 day?

(d) When did the plant grow the fastest in 1 day? What was the increase in height?

(e) How many days did the plant take to grow from 2 cm to 12 cm?

4. The line graph shows the number of visitors in a park between 6:00 a.m. and 10:00 a.m. on a Sunday morning. Study the graph and answer the questions which follow.

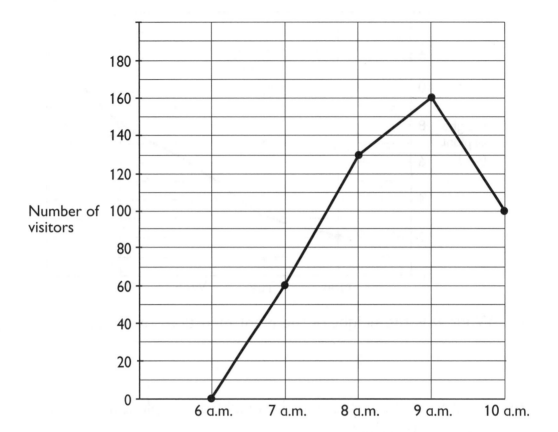

(a) At what time were there 60 visitors in the park?

(b) How many visitors were there in the park at 8:00 a.m.?

(c) When did the number of visitors increase by 30 in 1 hour?

(d) When did the number of visitors increase the most in 1 hour?

(e) When did the number of visitors decrease by 60 in 1 hour?

EXERCISE 37

1. This graph shows the exchange rate between Hong Kong dollars and Singapore dollars in a certain year.

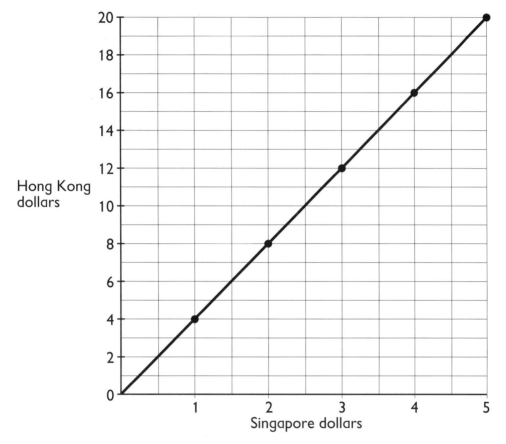

Study the graph and complete the following:

(a)

Singapore dollars	1	2		4	
Hong Kong dollars			12		20

(b) Hong Kong $10 could be exchanged for Singapore $_____.

(c) Singapore $4.50 could be exchanged for Hong Kong $_____.

2. A tap was turned on for 6 minutes to fill a tank with water. The line graph shows the volume of water in the tank at the end of each minute. Study the graph and answer the questions which follow.

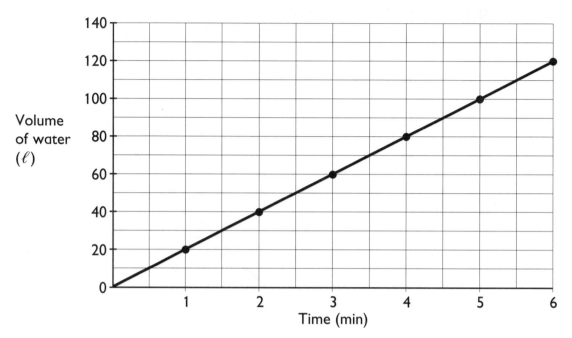

(a) How long did it take to fill the tank with 60 liters of water?

(b) How long did it take to fill the tank with 90 liters of water?

(c) How much water was in the tank at the end of 2 minutes?

(d) How much water was in the tank at the end of $3\frac{1}{2}$ minutes?

EXERCISE 38

1. The following figures are not drawn to scale.

    (a) Find ∠ACB.

    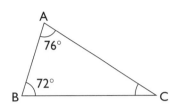

    (b) Find ∠TRS.

    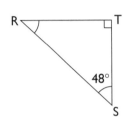

    (c) Find ∠LMK.

    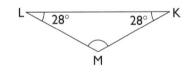

    (d) Find ∠FGH.

    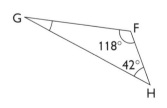

EXERCISE 39

1. The following figures are not drawn to scale. Find the unknown marked angles. Then mark each right-angled triangle with a ✓.

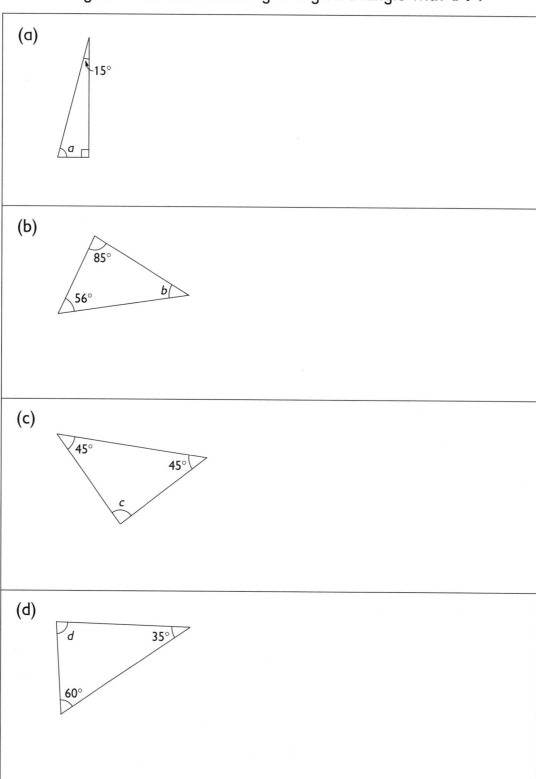

(a)

15°

a

(b)

85°

56°

b

(c)

45°

45°

c

(d)

d

35°

60°

EXERCISE 40

1. The following figures are not drawn to scale.

(a) DBC is a straight line.
Find ∠ABD.

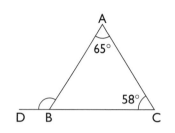

(b) WXY is a straight line.
Find ∠WXZ.

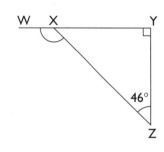

(c) ABD is a straight line.
Find ∠BDC.

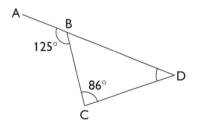

(d) STU is a straight line.
Find ∠SRT.

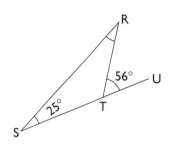

EXERCISE 41

1. The following figures are not drawn to scale. Find the unknown marked angles. Then mark each isosceles triangle with a ✓.

(a)

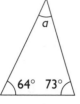

(b)

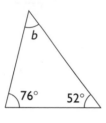

(c)

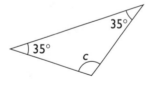

(d)

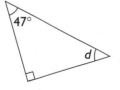

EXERCISE 42

1. The following figures are not drawn to scale. Find the unknown marked angles. Then mark each equilateral triangle with a ✓.

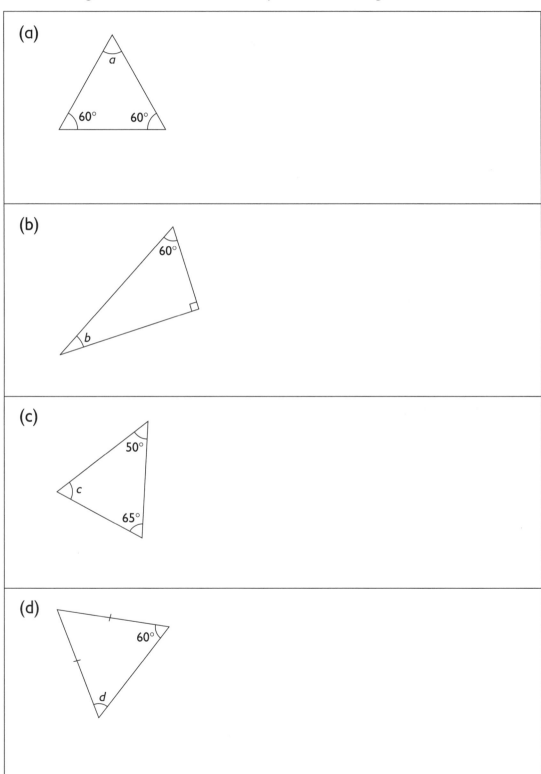

(a)

60°   60°   a

(b)

60°   b

(c)

50°   c   65°

(d)

60°   d

EXERCISE 43

1. The following figures are not drawn to scale. Find the unknown marked angles.

(a)

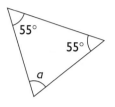

(b)

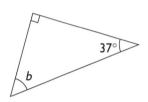

(c) BCD is a straight line.

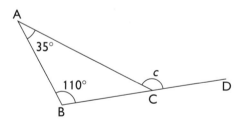

(d)

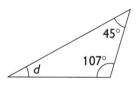

72

(e) ACD is a straight line.

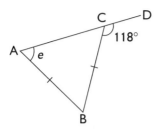

(f) ABC is a straight line.

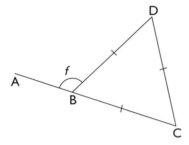

(g) DCB is a straight line.

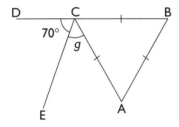

(h) BCD is a straight line.

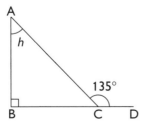

EXERCISE 44

1. Draw a triangle ABC in which AB = 5 cm, ∠CAB = 56° and ∠CBA = 78°.

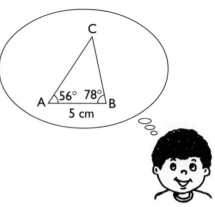

A   B

2. Draw a triangle XYZ in which XY = 6 cm, YZ = 4 cm and ∠XYZ = 90°.

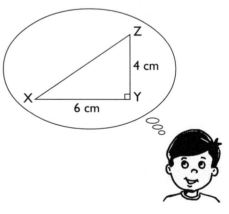

EXERCISE 45

1. The following parallelograms are not drawn to scale. Find the unknown marked angles.

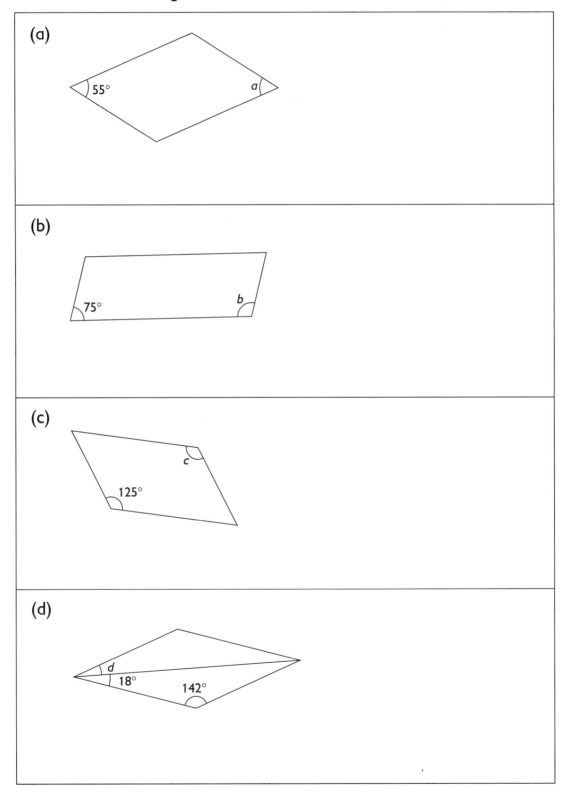

(a)

55°   a

(b)

75°   b

(c)

c

125°

(d)

d
18°
142°

(e)

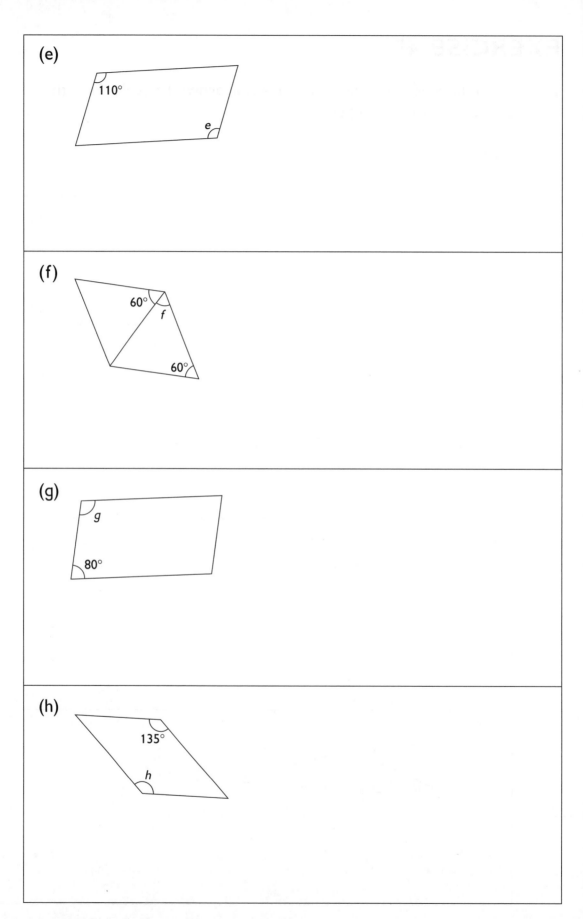

110°

e

(f)

60°

f

60°

(g)

g

80°

(h)

135°

h

EXERCISE 46

1. The following rhombuses are not drawn to scale. Find the unknown marked angles.

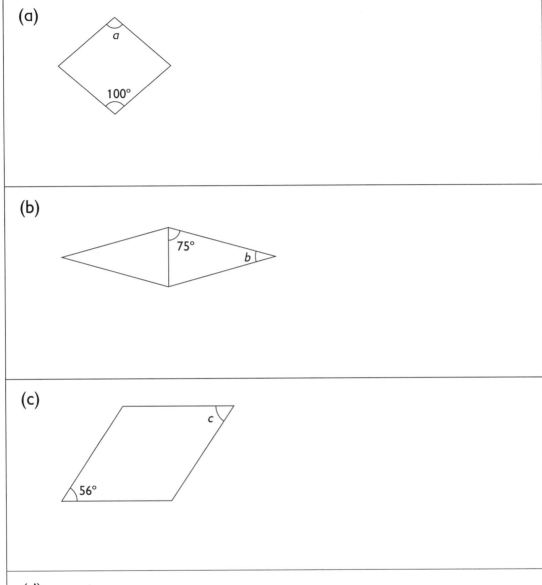

(a)

a

100°

(b)

75°

b

(c)

c

56°

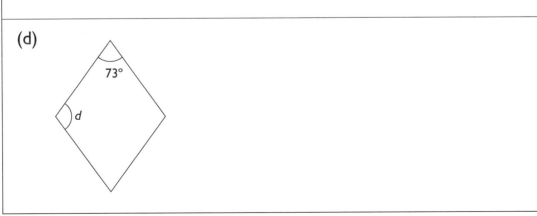

(d)

73°

d

(e)

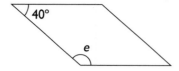

40°

e

(f)

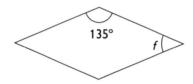

135°

f

(g)

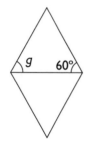

g   60°

(h)

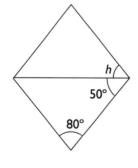

h

50°

80°

EXERCISE 47

1. The following trapezoids are not drawn to scale. Find the unknown marked angles.

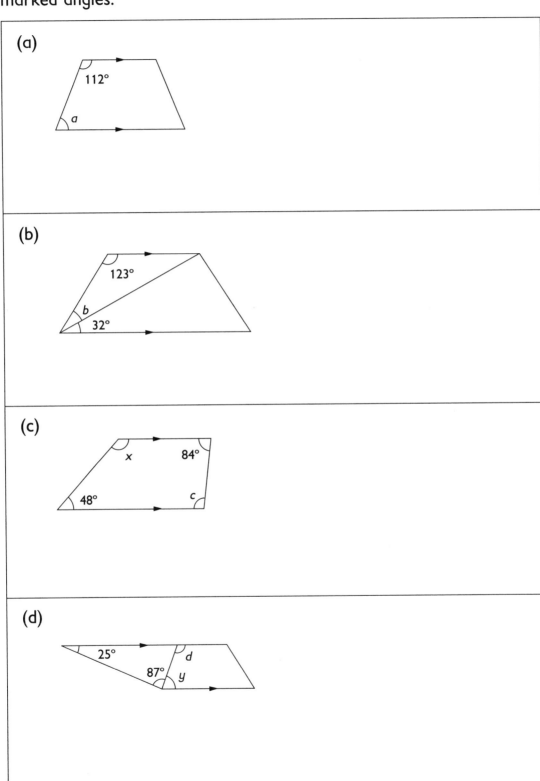

(a)

112°

a

(b)

123°

b

32°

(c)

x   84°

48°   c

(d)

25°

87°   y

d

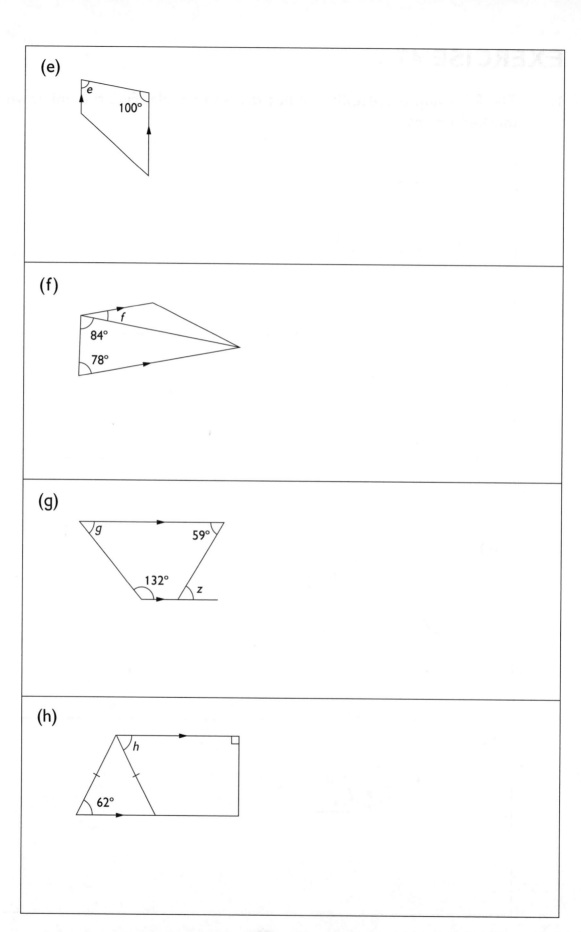

(e)

e

100°

(f)

f

84°

78°

(g)

g

59°

132°

z

(h)

h

62°

EXERCISE 48

1. Draw a parallelogram ABCD in which AB = 8 cm, BC = 5 cm and ∠ABC = 120°.

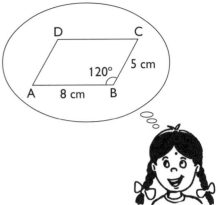

A   B

2. Draw a parallelogram PQRS in which PQ = 7 cm, PS = 6 cm and ∠SPQ = 45°.

3. Draw a rhombus ABCD in which AB = 6 cm and ∠DAB = 50°.

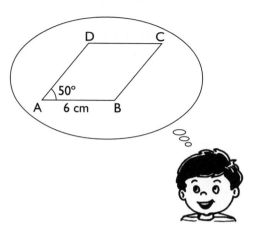

A   B

4. Draw a rhombus PQRS in which PQ = 5 cm and ∠SPQ = 120°.

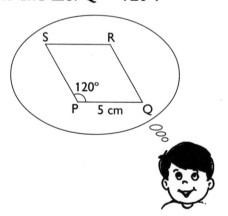

EXERCISE 49

1. Color the shape used in each of the following tessellations.
    (a) has been done for you.

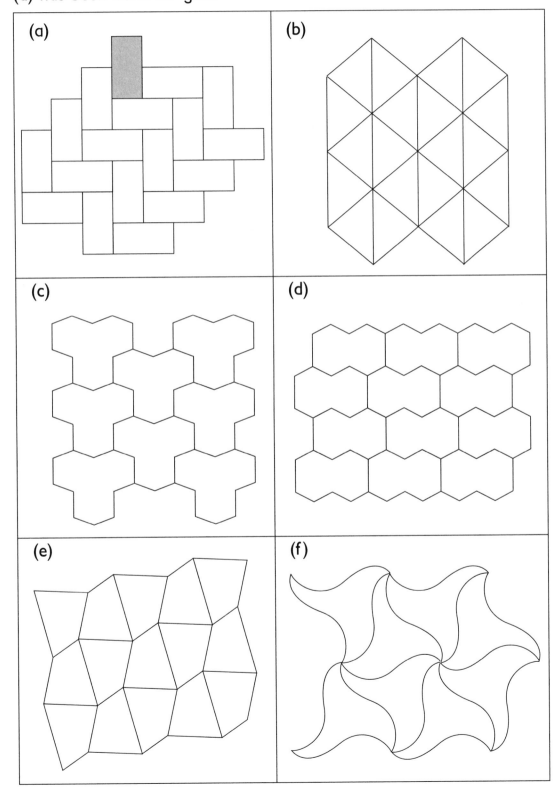

2. Extend each of the following tessellations in the space provided.

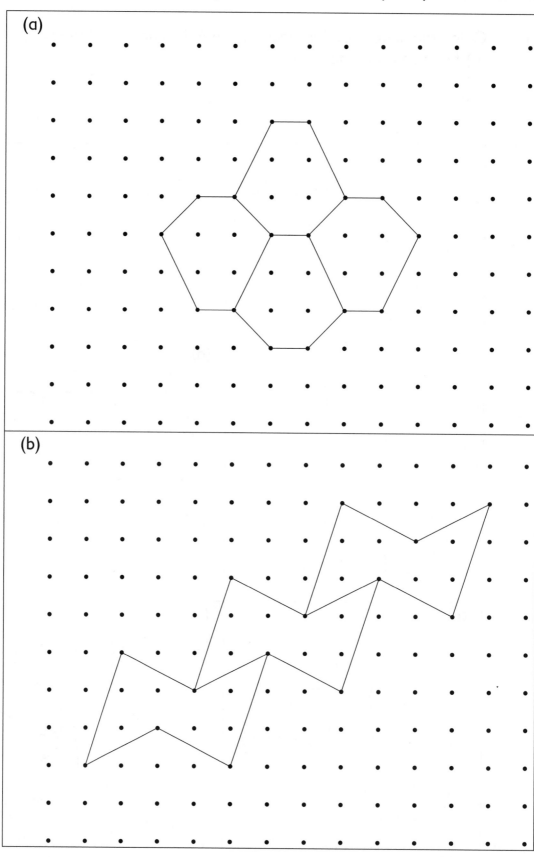

(a)

(b)

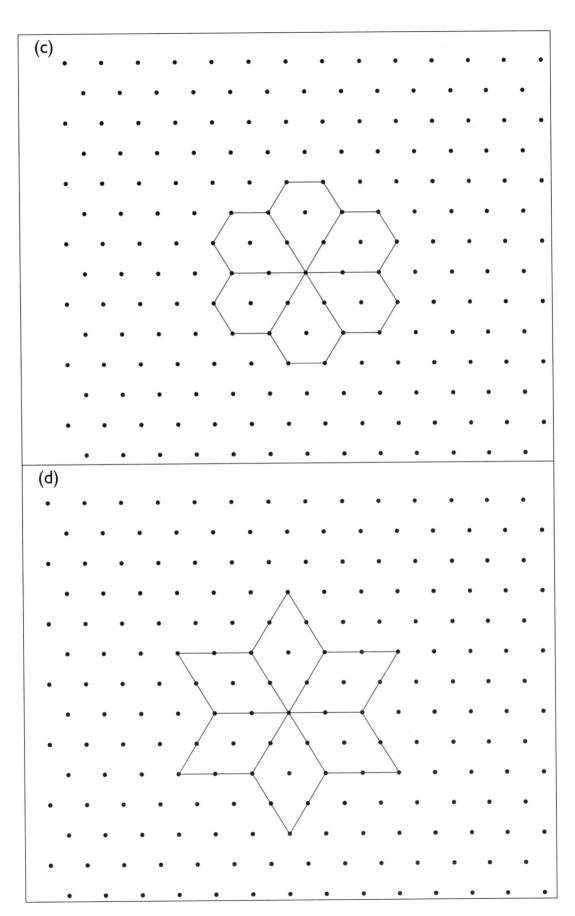

EXERCISE 50

1. Does each of the following shapes tessellate? Write **Yes** or **No**.

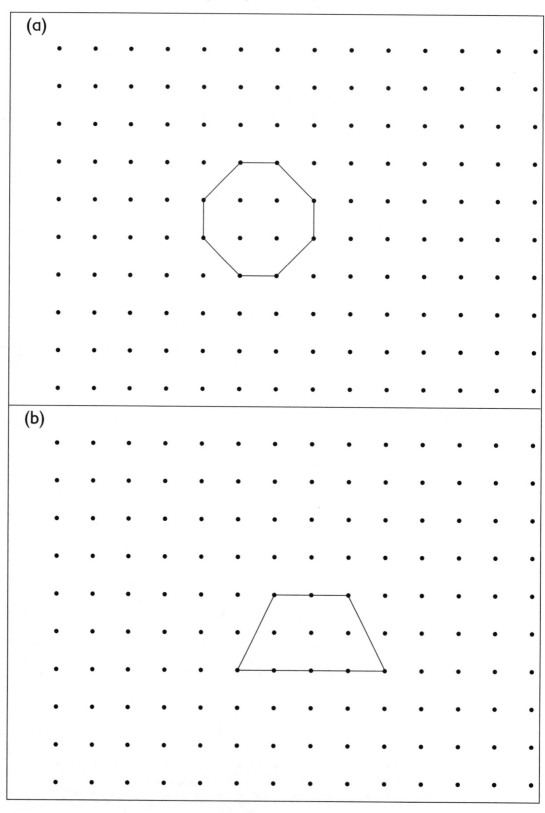

(a)

(b)

(c)

(d)

EXERCISE 51

1. In each of the following, use the given shape to make a tessellation in the space provided.

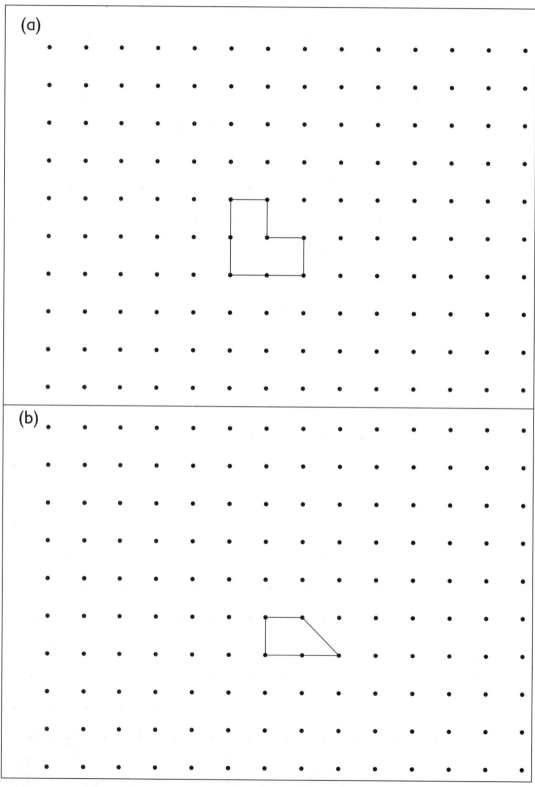

(c)

(d)

EXERCISE 52

1. Use the given shape to make two different tessellations in the spaces provided.

   (a) Tessellation 1

   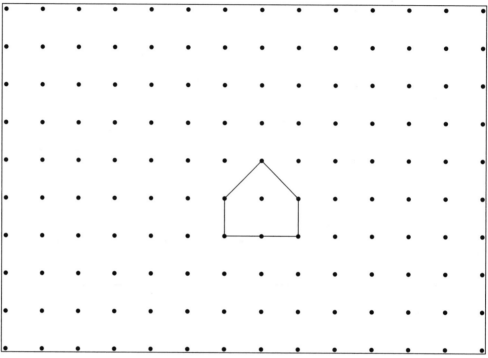

   (b) Tessellation 2

   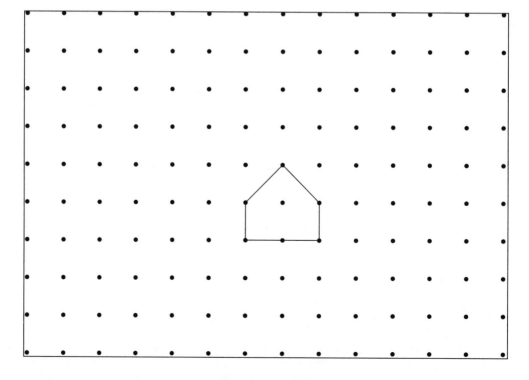

2. Use the given shape to make two different tessellations in the spaces provided.

(a) Tessellation 1

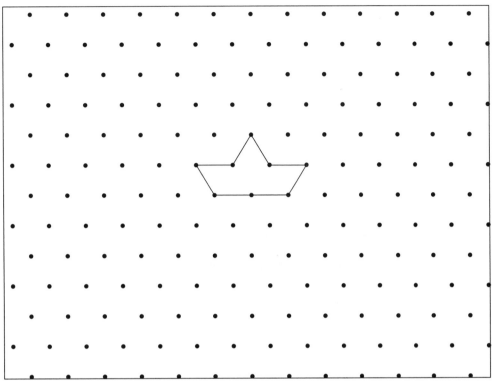

(b) Tessellation 2

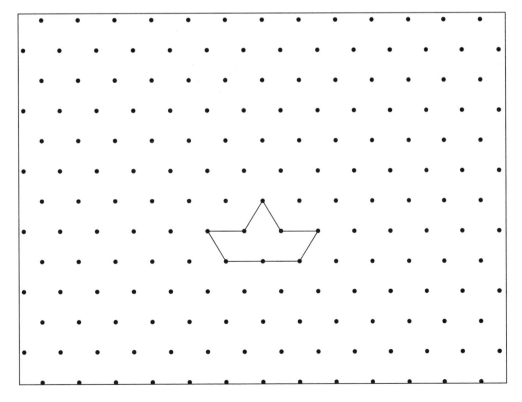

REVIEW 2

Write the answers in the boxes.

1. Complete the following table.

Decimals	0.5	0.8			0.48
Fractions	$\frac{1}{2}$		$\frac{3}{4}$		
Percentage	50%			35%	

2. In a group of 20 children, 7 of them wear glasses.

    (a) What percentage of the children wear glasses?

    (b) What percentage of the children do not wear glasses?

3. What percentage of $2 is 80 cents?

4. Find the value of each of the following:

    (a) 10% of $250

    (b) 75% of $1400

5. Hillary had $240. She spent 35% of the money. How much money had she left?

6. A vase cost $160. It was sold at 15% above the cost price. Find the selling price.

7. Gary had $12. He spent 25% of the money on food and 20% of it on transport. How much money had he left?

8. Mary had $50. She spent 20% of the money on a book and 15% of the remainder on a magazine.

   (a) Find the cost of the book.

   (b) Find the cost of the magazine.

9. Sally took 8 minutes to type 416 words. Her rate of typing was

   [   ] words per minute.

10. Alan spends $300 every 2 months. At this rate, how much will he spend in half a year?

11. Ryan and his friends rented a boat for $5 per hour. How many hours did they rent the boat for if they paid $35 altogether?

12. The rates of charges for renting a tennis court are as follows:

Monday to Friday	$3.50 per hour
Saturday and Sunday	$5.00 per hour

   (a) David rented the tennis court for 3 hours on Wednesday. How much did he have to pay?

   (b) Jim rented the tennis court on Tuesday and Saturday. He paid a total of $22. If he rented the tennis court for 2 hours on Tuesday, how many hours did he rent the tennis court for on Saturday?

13. Find the unknown marked angle in each of the following figures.

(a) ACD is a straight line.

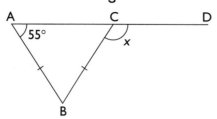

(b) ABC is a straight line.

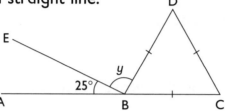

(c) ABC is a straight line.

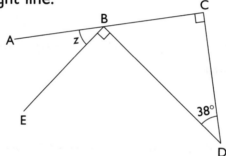

14. In the figure, not drawn to scale, ABCD is a parallelogram, BCE is a straight line and ∠BAD = 108°. Find ∠DCE.

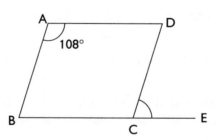

15. In the figure, not drawn to scale, PQRS is a parallelogram, RT ⊥ PS and ∠PQR = 55°. Find ∠TRS.

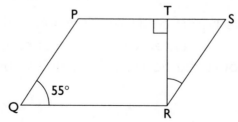

16. The total cost of 4 kg of prawns and 3 kg of fish is $76.50. If 1 kg of prawns costs $12.75, find the cost of 1 kg of fish.

17. A farmer had 60 pineapples. He sold $\frac{4}{5}$ of them at $3 each. He sold the rest at 3 for $1. How much money did he receive altogether?

18. The ratio of the number of books that Lina had to the number of books that Suling had was 1 : 2. After Lina bought 24 new books, the ratio became 2 : 1. How many books did Lina have at first?

---

19. Use the given shape to make a tessellation in the space provided.

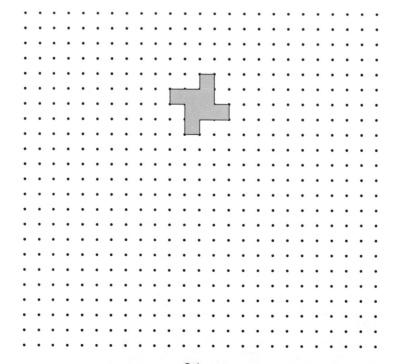

EXERCISE 53

1. Find the length of one edge of the cube.

Volume = 64 cm³

2. Find the unknown edge of each cuboid.

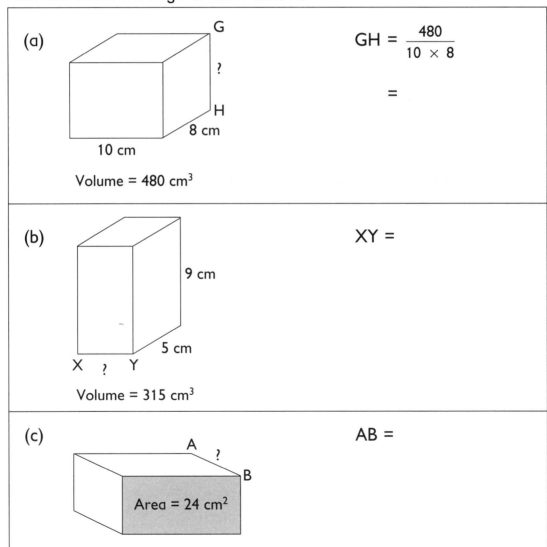

(a)

G

?

H

8 cm

10 cm

Volume = 480 cm³

$$GH = \frac{480}{10 \times 8}$$

$$=$$

(b)

9 cm

5 cm

X   ?   Y

Volume = 315 cm³

$$XY =$$

(c)

A   ?

B

Area = 24 cm²

Volume = 96 cm³

$$AB =$$

3. The base of a rectangular container measures 20 cm by 15 cm. The container contains 900 cm³ of water. Find the height of the water level in the container.

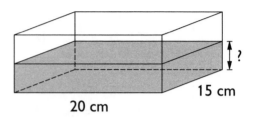

15 cm

20 cm

4. The base area of a rectangular tank is 6 m². The tank contains 15 m³ of water. What is the height of the water level in the tank?

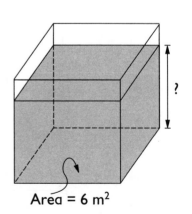

?

Area = 6 m²

EXERCISE 54

1. A rectangular container measuring 12 in. by 10 in. by 11 in. is completely filled with water. After 240 in.³ of water are taken out from the tank, what is the height of the water level in the container?

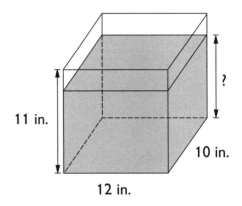

2. A rectangular tank, 40 cm long and 25 cm wide, contains water to a depth of 15 cm. After 2 liters of water are taken out from the tank, what is the height of the water level in the tank? (1 ℓ = 1000 cm³)

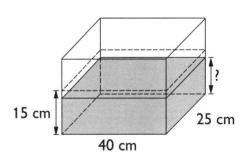

EXERCISE 55

1. A rectangular container, 20 cm long and 15 cm wide, contained some water. When an iron ball was put in, the water level rose by 3 cm. Find the volume of the iron ball.

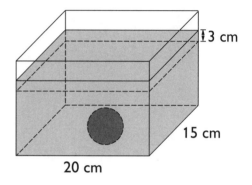

2. A rectangular container, 20 cm long and 10 cm wide, contained some water and a stone. When the stone was taken out, the water level dropped from 12 cm to 10 cm. Find the volume of the stone.

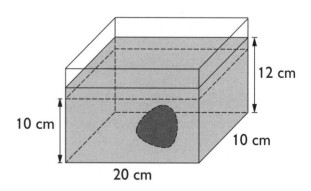

REVIEW 3

Write the answers in the boxes.

1. Find the value of each of the following:

    (a) $120 - 20 \div 5$

    (b) $6 \times 2 + 8 \div 2 \times 4$

    (c) 7.12×10

    (d) $5.6 \div 100$

2. Write the value of $\dfrac{2}{100} + \dfrac{6}{10} + 5 + \dfrac{9}{1000}$ as a decimal.

3. In 50.163, the value of the digit 6 is equal to $6 \times$ 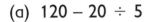. What is the missing number in the ■?

4. Which one of the following numbers is 4 when rounded off to the nearest whole number?

    3.75,   3.07,   4.52,   4.99

5. Which one of the following numbers has 4 as its factor?

    18,   34,   38,   64

6. Find the value of $196 \div 12$ correct to 1 decimal place.

7. Express $2\dfrac{4}{9}$ as a decimal correct to 2 decimal places.

8. Arrange the fractions in increasing order.

    $\dfrac{3}{4}$, $\dfrac{3}{5}$, $\dfrac{5}{7}$

9. How many minutes are there in $2\dfrac{1}{3}$ hours?

101

10. A bottle contains 1.2 liters of fruit juice. Express the amount of fruit juice in milliliters.

11. In a choir, there are 30 girls and 10 boys. What percentage of the children are boys?

12. Express 7% as a decimal.

13. Express 36% as a fraction in its simplest form.

14. The membership fee of a club was $5 last year. It was increased by 20% this year. Find the new membership fee.

15. In the figure, not drawn to scale, ABC and BDC are right-angled triangles, $\angle ACD = 35°$ and $\angle DBC = 40°$. Find $\angle BAC$.

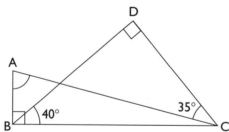

16. In the figure, not drawn to scale, PQRS is a trapezoid, TR = TS and $\angle RST = 74°$. Find $\angle QRT$.

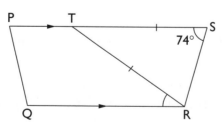

17. The figure shows a solid made up of 2-cm cubes. Find its volume.

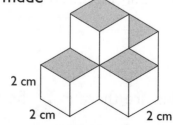

2 cm

2 cm   2 cm

18.

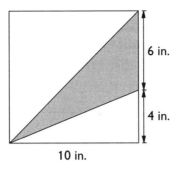

6 in.

4 in.

10 in.

(a) Find the area of the shaded part of the square.

(b) What is the ratio of the area of the shaded part to the area of the unshaded part? Give the answer in its simplest form.

19. A tap was turned on to fill an empty tank with water. The graph shows the amount of water in the tank at regular intervals of time. Use the graph to answer the questions below.

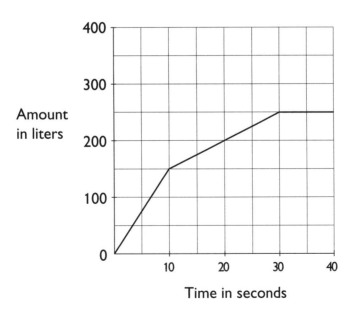

Amount in liters

Time in seconds

(a) What was the amount of water that had collected in the tank by the first 10 seconds?

(b) What was the capacity of the tank?

20. David and Peter had $90 and $200 respectively. They were each given an equal amount of money. Then Peter had twice as much money as David. How much money did each boy receive?

---

21. Gopal spent $\frac{3}{5}$ of his money in the first week and $\frac{1}{3}$ of the remainder in the second week. He spent $110 altogether. How much money had he left?